Jen P...

by Liza Charlesworth

ISBN: 978-1-338-84419-1

Art Director: Tannaz Fassihi; Designer: Cynthia Ng; Illustrated by Kevin Zimmer
Copyright © Liza Charlesworth. All rights reserved. Published by Scholastic Inc.

3 4 5 6 7 68 26 25 24

Printed in Jiaxing, China. First printing, June 2022.

It is Jen!
Jen is a pen.

Jen Pen can draw in red.

3

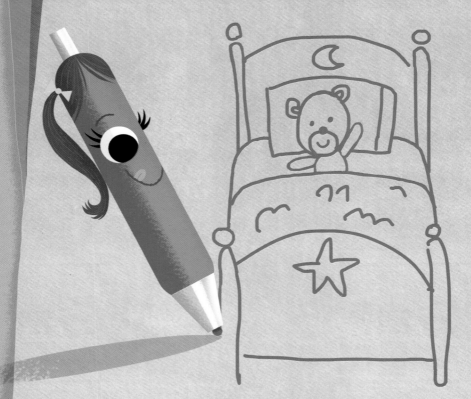

Can Jen Pen draw a bed?
Yes, Jen Pen can!

Can Jen Pen draw a web?
Yes, Jen Pen can!

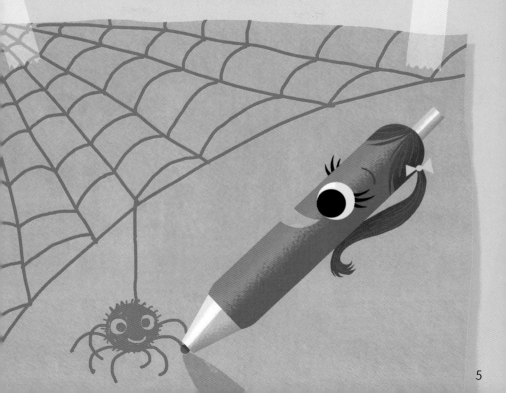

Can Jen Pen draw men?
Yes, Jen Pen can!

Jen Pen can draw
a set of ten!

Can Jen draw a fox in a den?
Yes, Jen Pen can!

Can Jen Pen draw a pet hen?
Yes, Jen Pen can!

"I am Bev!" said the pet hen.

Can Jen Pen draw a jet?
Yes, Jen Pen can!

Can Jen Pen and Bev Hen
get on the jet?
Yes, they can!

BYE, Jen Pen!
BYE, Bev Hen!

Read & Review

Invite your learner to point to each short-e word and read it aloud.

red

den

ten

Bev

pen

men

pet

jet

bed

hen

yes

get

Jen

set

web

15

Fun Fill-Ins

Read the sentences aloud, inviting your learner to complete them using the short-e words in the box.

pen   jet   hen   red   men

1. Jen is a _____.

2. Jen can draw in the color _____.

3. Jen can draw ten _____.

4. Jen can draw a pet _____.

5. Jen and the hen get

   on a _____.